BUMPER BOOK 1994

FRED BASSET

by ALEX GRAHAM

Express delivery!

29/9 GRAHAM

Orion Books Ltd
Orion House
5 Upper St Martin's Lane
London WC2H 9EA

First published by Orion 1994

Black and white drawings by Michael Martin

© Associated Newspapers plc 1994

ISBN 1 85797 932 X

Printed and bound in Italy

2.60

C000162859

Each of us has his own style... Yorky's the dashing, sporty type...

...Jock the go-anywhere family model...

...And me... good runner, one careful owner

119

Off to the office he goes, geared up for a day of vital decision-making

Will it be the cheese and pickle sandwich first or the egg and tomato?

120

A subtle hint that it's my dinner-time is occasionally required

© Associated Newspapers Ltd., 1993

121

What a clever move

© Associated Newspapers Ltd., 1993

CHECKMATE

Third game in a row the vicar's won

122

Another pound for the Church Restoration Fund

CHURCH FUND

TELEPHONE... I'LL GET IT.

IT'S FOR YOU!
MERVYN LAWSON.

BERYL LAWSON WOULD LIKE A
WORD WITH YOU NOW.

Am I ever going
to get settled?

9/9 GRAHAM

I MUST SHOW YOU THE LATEST PHOTOGRAPH OF FRED.

It's a particularly good one.

OH, LOOK! HERE'S ONE OF A LITTLE VILLAGE WHERE WE STAYED ON OUR HOLIDAY.

THIS IS A NICE ONE. THE GARDEN OF OUR HOTEL... AND ANOTHER OF THE SWIMMING POOL.

WE MET A CHARMING COUPLE. THIS IS THEM ON THE BEACH. TOM AND JANE WOLTER. AND HERE'S ONE OF THEM AT DINNER.

WE THEN WENT FARTHER NORTH. HERE'S A SNAP OF THE MOUNTAINS.

THIS IS A PRETTY LITTLE COTTAGE NESTLED IN A CLEARING IN THE WOODS.

I suppose she might get around to me sometime!

ALEX GRAHAM

16/9

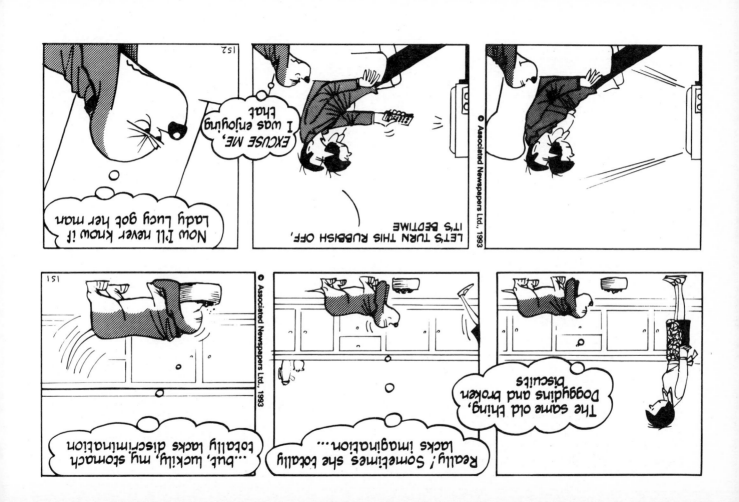

What a BRILLIANT move!

WHAT A BRILLIANT MOVE!

WAS IT?

It puts the vicar in a hopeless position

1990 Associated Newspapers Ltd

IT PUTS ME IN A HOPELESS POSITION.

DOES IT?

He'll have to resign.

I'LL HAVE TO RESIGN.

WILL YOU?

CONGRATULATIONS! A STROKE OF GENIUS!

A happy fluke!

ALEX GRAHAM 4/11

PLEASE ... DON'T MOVE.

Of course I must. After all it's your chair.

THANK YOU VERY MUCH! ARE YOU SURE YOU WON'T BE UNCOMFORTABLE DOWN THERE ON THE FLOOR?

How could I refuse when he was so nice about it?

PLEASE DON'T DISTURB YOURSELF. I CAN SEE YOU'RE COMFORTABLE.

DON'T GET UP JUST BECAUSE I'VE HAD A TIRING DAY AND WANT TO SIT DOWN.

I insist!

Come on now, Fred....

Chin up, chest out, shoulders back

134

Passed with flying colours, my annual check-up

VETERINARY SURGERY

Rumour has it that this chap is a big bully

133

Well, me, Jock and Yorky are going to teach him a lesson....

... aren't we, lads?

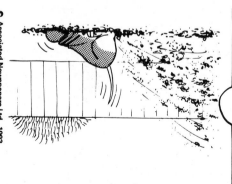

COME ON, FRED. It was a challenge, I couldn't resist!

The summit! At last — I'VE MADE IT!

Driving myself to the limit of endurance. Almost there!

Risking life and limb.

Because it's there!

Why do I tackle this hazardous ascent?

We've had a wasted afternoon

It took an hour to find a parking space, we've searched in all the shops...

...and we still haven't found a present for Auntie Winnifred

Associated Newspapers Ltd., 1993

He's badly in need of inspiration

Only three more shopping days to go...

Associated Newspapers Ltd., 1993

...and he still hasn't a clue what to get her for Christmas

JUST GOING TO
TAKE FRED
FOR A WALK.

Victory.

17-11
ALEX
GRAHAM

The first tasting of his home-made rhubarb wine.

HOW IS IT THIS YEAR?

SAME AS USUAL!

They serve it to people they don't like.

© 1991 Tribune Media Services, Inc.
All Rights Reserved

© 1991 Associated Newspapers Ltd

© 1991 Tribune Media Services, Inc.
All Rights Reserved

26/5

'A new year, a new man', he said

'I'll share the chores with you', he said

171

The new man has lasted a week

© Associated Newspapers Ltd., 1994

The perils of modern motoring...

© Associated Newspapers Ltd., 1994

...cut up at the roundabout, nearly rammed at the junction...

...and, to add insult to injury, we've been ambushed by the Tucker twins

172

177

178

ARE YOU ALL RIGHT SITTING LIKE THAT?

YES, I'M FINE

YOU LOOK SO UNCOMFORTABLE, ARE YOU SURE FRED'S NOT IN THE WAY?

NO, REALLY I'M QUITE ALL RIGHT

I THINK YOU SHOULD MOVE HIM

Didn't you hear, she's perfectly happy where she is

YES, THE SNOOTY ONE SAID...

This could take a long time

Her friend Jean's back from holiday and she's filling her in on the gossip

AND THE UPSHOT WAS...

She's been an hour and they're only up to last Tuesday

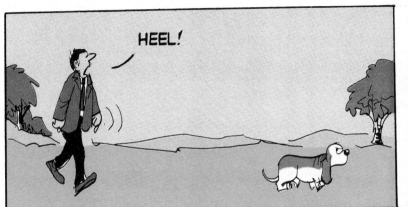

IT'S YOUR FAULT! NO, IT ISN'T!

An argument. Only one thing for it...

WHAT'S WRONG WITH FRED?

HE'S HURT HIS PAW

POOR FRED

OH DEAR, IT MUST BE A THORN

It always works

Jock's being rude to a perfect stranger

It's not really like him at all

It must have something to do with him wearing his clan tartan

© Associated Newspapers Ltd., 1994

191

192

Ah!

I win!

You blinked!

Deep in enemy territory...

So I must be careful!

They might be lurking anywhere.

Ready to pounce ... A sudden ambush.

So I'm advancing behind a protective screen of crack mobile troops.

ALEX GRAHAM
18/8

Yorky may be small, but he has that indefinable quality that stamps him as a natural leader.

Personality .... character... call it what you will.

Napoleon had it.

He was a little fellow, too!

25/8

ALEX GRAHAM

Marvellous film! This shepherd's lying helpless at the bottom of the cliff with a broken leg!

And he's sent his faithful dog off for help!

There goes Spot! Leaping from crag to crag ... swimming across the river ... racing full out through the forest!

And I would do the same for him.

ALEX GRAHAM 1/9

Though it might take a little longer.

It must be something in Jock's Highland blood

205

Occasionally, he likes to elevate himself...

...so he can look down his nose at us common Sassenachs

© Associated Newspapers Ltd., 1994

Dinner for two at eight

© Associated Newspapers Ltd., 1994

And leftovers for one at eight-thirty

206

He's off for a hard day at the office, she's off to slave over a hot stove...

...and I'm off into the garden...

...for a hard day's digging

© Associated Newspapers Ltd., 1994

A nice little dog chasing his tail

© Associated Newspapers Ltd., 1994

I don't do that sort of thing myself

I can barely see my tail, let alone chase it

He's got that bonfire going well

213

And the other one's going well, too...

...where he put his pipe in his jacket pocket

That's the third cat I've chased up this tree today

214

There's quite a colony of them up there now

BED!

You don't really mean it...

...do you?

BED!

Yes, he does

© Associated Newspapers Ltd., 1994

215

FRED, WHAT HAVE YOU DONE TO YOURSELF?

© Associated Newspapers Ltd., 1994

HAVE YOU BEEN IN A FIGHT?

I'm almost too embarrassed to tell. I was gaining on this rabbit...

...when I tripped over my ears, did a somersault and landed on my nose

216

BONJOUR, MADAME, VOUS ÊTES TRÈS BELLE...

Jean-Claude calls regularly with his onions. He's such a charmer

A BIENTÔT

And every time she buys two strings of onions she doesn't need

© Associated Newspapers Ltd., 1994

Ah, one of those Tibetan types

I'd like to introduce myself...

© Associated Newspapers Ltd., 1994

...but I don't know which end to say hello to

I've been shampooed, combed and brushed...

I've been poked all over by complete strangers...

...and look who gets all the credit!

DOG SHOW

© Associated Newspapers Ltd., 1994

225

WE WON! BEST OF BREED, WE GOT THE SILVER CUP

OH, WELL DONE, FRED. THE TROPHY DESERVES PRIDE OF PLACE IN THE CABINET

226

© Associated Newspapers Ltd., 1994

That puts his darts medal into perspective

BEST OF BREED